DESERT DOGS
Coyotes, Foxes & Wolves

FEW RELATIONSHIPS are as filled with love and hate as the bond that ties mankind to the canines. From some unknown point in history wild canines diverged along two paths—one group becoming our devoted and useful companions,

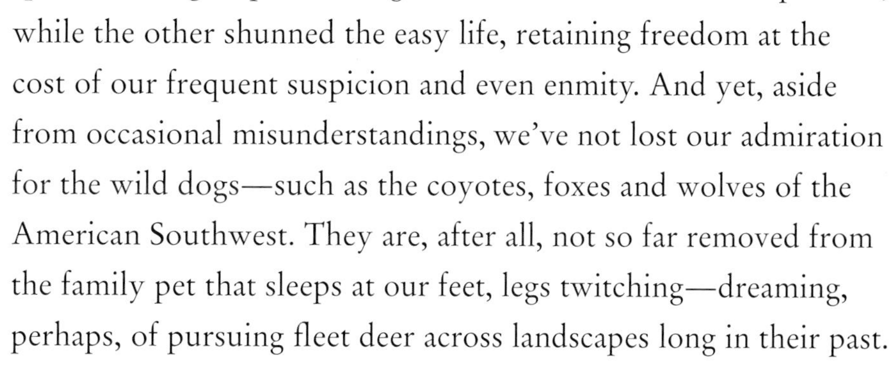

while the other shunned the easy life, retaining freedom at the cost of our frequent suspicion and even enmity. And yet, aside from occasional misunderstandings, we've not lost our admiration for the wild dogs—such as the coyotes, foxes and wolves of the American Southwest. They are, after all, not so far removed from the family pet that sleeps at our feet, legs twitching—dreaming, perhaps, of pursuing fleet deer across landscapes long in their past.

Mexican wolves (above) are the most endangered of the Southwestern wild canines which also include coyotes (left), kit fox (opposite) and the gray fox.

It's a Dog's Lifezone

Imagine climbing aboard a time machine in the Southwest, and setting the dial back about three million years. You emerge in the epoch we call the Pliocene, to a landscape startlingly different from today's desert environment. A tropical forest towers over you—immense, broad-leaved trees shade dim glades choked with ferns; brilliant orchids sprout through mosses hung like drapes over the limbs of giant figs and cypresses.

The most "southwestern" of the Southwest's canines is the kit fox, whose range closely parallels that of its preferred prey, kangaroo rats.

Your eye catches a flash of movement, and you look to see an animal scampering cat-like up the trunk of a nearby tree, its feline agility enhanced by sharp, retractable claws. This primitive carnivore belongs to a group of animals called miacids, the ancestors of modern cats *and* dogs. If you climbed back in the time machine and set it on fast forward, you could watch through the succeeding eons as the miacids split off into their separate lines—the felids generally retaining their climbing talents and retractable claws, while the canids developed more earth-bound skills.

Today the Sonoran Desert region encompasses a tremendous variety of habitats, from sparsely vegetated low-elevation deserts, to the relatively lush upland deserts of palo verde trees and saguaro cactus, and up through grasslands, oak woodlands and coniferous forests on the mountain peaks. Four of the dog-like descendants of the miacids are indigenous to this landscape: the coyote (*Canis latrans*), the Mexican gray wolf (*Canis lupus baileyi*), the kit fox (*Vulpes macrotis*) and the gray fox (*Urocyon cinereoargenteus*). Though evolution has led them down separate paths, they share kinship with each other—and indeed, through that distant ancestor, with the bobcats and mountain lions that also prowl the Southwest.

The diminutive kit fox is probably the most specialized of our "desert dogs." Only four to five pounds when full grown—picture a fox the size of a small house cat—its range closely parallels that of the kangaroo rats that form a large part of its diet. It is truly a Southwestern animal, occurring in the deserts of Arizona, New Mexico, Utah, Nevada and California, plus Mexico, with overlaps into a few bordering states (a closely related species, the swift fox, inhabits the Great Plains).

The kit fox prefers flat areas of loose soil for excavating its burrows and is usually found below 4,500' elevation. Like

Coyotes are famous for their adaptability, so it's not unusual to spot them in unlikely places, like this one foraging in the high tide line of Laguna San Ignacio in Baja California Sur.

the rodents it hunts, it is almost strictly nocturnal, and thus hardly ever glimpsed by humans. Its tiny size accentuates its most notable feature: huge ears that look as though they could target a mouse nibbling seeds from a hundred yards away.

While the kit fox's specialist habitat and diet naturally restrict its range, the West's most famous canid apparently wasn't satisfied with being just *the West's* most famous canid. Despite the all-out war waged against it for the last 100 years, mostly by government predator-control agents, the coyote has not only survived, it has actually expanded its population and its range. Before the European discovery of America, the coyote lived within a swath that extended from central Mexico to southern Canada, bordered on the east by the Great Plains and on the west by the Rocky Mountains. By 1940, despite traps, poison and guns, it had expanded north into Alaska and east to the Great Lakes states. Presently the range of the coyote includes all the lower 48 states, about half of Canada and Alaska, plus all of Mexico and a good deal of Central America.

FAMED WESTERN HUNTER J. FRANK DOBIE ONCE POINTED OUT THAT THE COYOTE'S FAVORITE FOOD IS ANYTHING HE CAN CHEW.

The coyote's supreme adaptability is largely responsible for this success. As predator-control programs in the early part of this century achieved victory against species such as wolves, mountain lions and bears, coyotes filled some of the niches left vacant. The creation of vast expanses of grazing and croplands also indirectly benefited the coyote, since these new habitats proved ideal for some rodents, a mainstay of the coyote diet. Also, when a coyote population is stressed by extermination efforts, their reproductive rate increases—ironically, the campaign against them might have contributed to their expansion.

In the Southwest coyotes can be found in virtually any habitat, from the driest deserts to grasslands to pine and fir forests—and well within the limits of many cities. It is with the saguaro-studded desert, though, that they seem inextricably linked, serenading the sunset with an off-key chorus of yaps and howls.

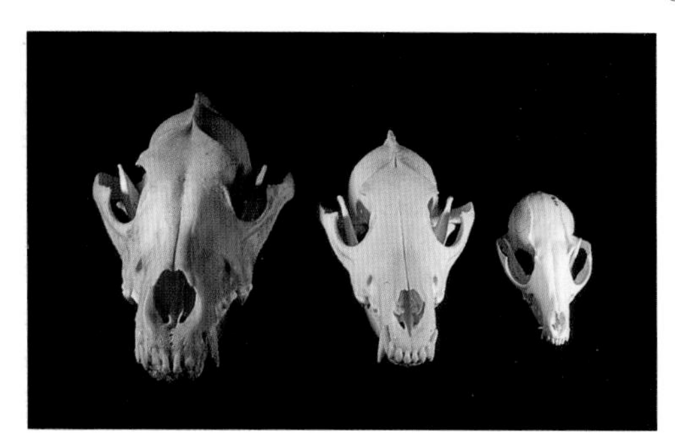

LEFT TO RIGHT: Mexican wolf, coyote and gray fox. The much larger wolf skull accomodates immensely powerful jaws—trappers reported captive wolves tearing apart metal buckets or biting through thin chains.

Southwestern coyotes are smaller than their cold-weather relatives, averaging no more than 25 pounds, compared to 40 or more for a northern animal (this is a common variation among species with members that inhabit different climates—a smaller body is easier to keep cool, a larger one easier to keep warm).

The gray fox is not as famous as the coyote—no one sells pastel fox silhouettes with neckerchiefs—but it is nearly as widespread. While barely reaching into Canada, the gray fox can be found in most of the 48 states except for the upper Great Plains and Northwest, and extends all the

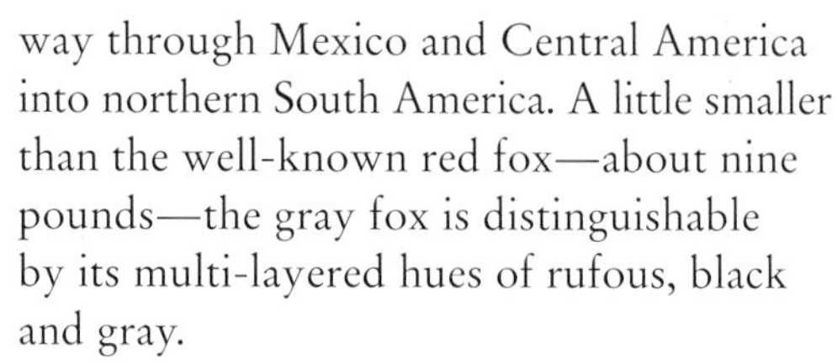

way through Mexico and Central America into northern South America. A little smaller than the well-known red fox—about nine pounds—the gray fox is distinguishable by its multi-layered hues of rufous, black and gray.

In the Sonoran Desert region gray foxes are found from deserts up to oak woodlands, in terrain that provides rock crevices or fallen trees for shelter. Unlike the coyote, gray foxes from the desert display no obvious physical differences from their eastern and northern kin. And all gray foxes share a talent passed down from their miacid forbears—a very un-doglike tree climbing ability.

In sad counterpoint to the wide-ranging gray fox and coyote is the near-extinction of the Mexican wolf. Never a true "desert" species, the Mexican wolf, a smaller subspecies of the gray wolf, historically ranged through the high country of Mexico, southern New Mexico, southwestern Texas and southeastern Arizona, especially in oak and pine-oak woodlands. Hit hard by poison and trapping, wolves were nearly eliminated in the U.S. by the 1920s. The last wolves recorded in the U.S. were killed in Arizona, New Mexico and Texas between 1966 and 1970.

In the 1970s and 1980s public attitudes toward

A gray fox hunts the oak woodlands of southeastern Arizona's Chiricahua Mountains.

Recovering a Lost Species

Mexican wolves were declared endangered in 1976; by 1982 the U.S. and Mexico approved a recovery plan developed by an international team. Wolves captured in Mexico and Arizona provided the beginning for a breeding program at facilities across the U.S. and Mexico, including the Arizona-Sonora Desert Museum. Today there are over 130 animals in the program, and some may one day be used in a U.S. Fish and Wildlife reintroduction effort in Arizona and New Mexico. Hopes continue that natural re-establishment might also occur.

Unconfirmed wolf sightings in southern Arizona, New Mexico and Texas have prompted wildlife agencies to conduct howling surveys. People are trained to howl like wolves, then listen for answers. So far, only coyotes and dogs have replied.

wolves began to change, and plans were drawn to save the Mexican wolf. Five wolves were live-trapped from a remnant population in the Sierra Madre of Mexico between 1977 and 1980; of these, two males and one pregnant female were used to start a captive breeding program, of which the Arizona-Sonora Desert Museum has been a part since the inception. Recently, other captive Mexican wolves from different bloodlines were added to the program. At present there is a healthy captive population of over 130 wolves, and plans are in the works for the first of several possible releases in Arizona and New Mexico.

It is possible the captive population now represents the last of the Mexican wolves. The area from which the breeding animals were taken might still harbor a few wolves, but the rugged terrain of the Sierra Madre is loath to reveal such secrets.

From five pound kit fox to sixty-five pound Mexican wolf, the ranges of these four diverse canids overlap only in the Southwest—a testimony to its strikingly varied terrain and habitats.

Family Life

On a crisp spring morning, the rising sun casts warm light on the side of a brush-covered hill. Under an overhanging boulder, almost invisible, is a small tunnel, the well-packed dirt of its entrance patterned with scores of overlapping footprints. Though the interior is dark, dawn illuminates the quartet of tiny, round faces that appear in the opening, blinking sleepily at the brightness.

The tiny kit fox is a master excavator.

The pups hesitate at the brink of the slope, until a low whine from the brush in front of the tunnel acts as a trigger and they spill helter-skelter over the edge, sliding to the dry wash at the base of the hill. One pup immediately pounces on another and they wrestle, snarling furious puppy snarls. Another finds a well-gnawed bone and drags it off, pursued by the fourth pup until that one spots a dead leaf tumbling along the ground and crouches to stalk the prey. Meanwhile their mother, who emerged from the den in advance to scout for hazards, watches over her litter carefully.

Though details might vary, this scene could be repeated for any of the species in this book. To a casual onlooker the activity might seem like simple fun—but that seemingly frivolous play serves several vital functions in the pups' development.

All canid puppies are altricial; that is, they are blind and helpless at birth and require complete care from their parents. Even after their eyes have opened and they can move around, they must be taught the hunting and social skills that will enable them to survive on their own. This strategy of prolonged parental care is typical among animals whose survival skills are not purely instinctive, but must be learned (such as humans).

Pups are born with the instinct to play. But as they chase and wrestle with each other, compete in tugs-of-war and pounce on butterflies and bits of fur, they are honing their muscles and coordination, gaining experience with depth perception and the trajectory of moving targets, and refining their senses of smell and hearing. The wrestling matches are also important in establishing a hierarchy of dominance—a vital facet of pack behavior.

Gray foxes are keen climbers and will often den in rock crevices.

Forever Wild

*W*ILD CANINES *and domestic dogs still share their ancient forebears' chromosomes, and cross-breeding is possible. Growing in popularity as household pets are wolf-hybrids, some boasting as much as 90% "timberwolf" blood, as well as "coy-dogs." But many problems arise from such crosses; the "wild" side of the dogs' heritage often prevails behaviorally, and once-cuddly puppies may turn into competitive or aggressive pack members. Sadly, many wild canid-domestic dog hybrids end up as unsuitable pets, destined for the pound or worse.*

Wolf hybrids have become popular but sometimes problematic pets.

A FAMILY OF FIVE KIT FOX PUPS CAN DEVOUR A POUND OF MEAT EVERY TWENTY-FOUR HOURS—WHICH ADDS UP TO 500–600 RODENTS THE PARENTS MUST CATCH DURING THE EIGHT-WEEK DENNING PERIOD.

Wolves are the most well-known pack animals. Because of the many myths that long surrounded wolf behavior the word "pack" developed negative connotations—a synonym for "gang." Instead, the wolf pack is a highly sophisticated social structure, a tightly knit cooperative union generally consisting of a lead, or alpha, pair and one or more subordinate individuals, usually offspring of the alpha pair from previous years. The subordinates help with hunting and feeding the current brood, but rarely breed.

Because Mexican wolves were nearly exterminated before they could be studied in the wild, we don't know very much about the structure of their packs, though it seems likely that Mexican wolf packs were not large since pack size is related to prey size. Their preferred prey, the diminutive Coues' whitetail deer or slightly larger mule deer, were relatively easy for one or two wolves to bring down, but were probably too small to keep a large pack well-fed. Recorded sightings of more than six Mexican wolves together were extremely rare, so it is likely the common unit of organization was the close family, consisting of a male and female and their offspring of that year, or bands of sibling yearlings traveling together.

Wolf dens in the Southwest were most likely similar to the den described above, probably located in oak woodlands. Mexican wolves bred in February or March, and an average of five pups were born in April or May. These would have stayed with their parents at least through the fall, learning the tricks of the wolf trade, then some or all of them may have set out to look for their own territories during the winter.

It is thought that, like wolves, coyotes may mate for life—but this is a difficult thing to prove in a wild population. Coyotes often form packs, with a similar structure to those of wolves, but there are coyotes that don't form packs or some packs that are only temporary breeding-season units; coyote pack-forming behavior varies widely depending on habitat, prey and hunting pressure. In a coyote pack, typically an alpha pair heads up a group of four to eight, including one to three beta members—offspring of the alpha pair from a previous litter. Beta females rarely breed, *unless* there is a sudden drop in the coyote population. In such cases, researchers have found that the beta female of a pack experiencing a loss of members not only will breed, she might even share the den of the alpha female (this stress-induced fertility is thought to be one of the reasons coyotes have prospered in the face of unrelenting persecution). Beta members also help defend the den and home territory of the pack, and they assist in hunting and caring for the young.

From the time they are born, pups such as this coyote are lavished with parental care.

Coyotes give birth once a year. The pups, usually five to ten, are born in April or early May after a gestation period identical to that of wolves—63 days. They don't leave the den until they are about three weeks old, but soon after they forsake it permanently. At around six weeks of age, when the pups begin cutting teeth, the parents introduce them to solid food—both regurgitated morsels and small rodents presented whole. As the pups grow, so does the size of the meal, until they are brought live pack rats and rabbits to chase and kill themselves. Soon after this they begin accompanying the adults on hunts.

In fall the pack usually undergoes some adjustments. One or more of the beta members might leave to roam until they join with other nomads to form a new pack; pack vacancies are filled by members of the current brood. Siblings of new beta members might strike out on their own as

well, skipping the apprenticeship year altogether. We don't know what controls the restructuring, but by winter the pack has stabilized and the breeding cycle begins anew.

Unlike their larger relatives, foxes do not form packs. Both their prey and their territories are small, so a large group would be a disadvantage. The basic social unit consists of a breeding pair and their current offspring, which strike out on their own as soon as they are fully developed. It's thought that gray foxes, and possibly kit foxes, usually find a new mate each year.

Gray foxes are much less likely to dig burrows than other Southwestern canids. More often they will use a rock crevice or hollow log or, in at least one observed case in the eastern U.S., a hole twenty feet up the trunk of a tree. But they will appropriate old badger burrows, suitably modified, and have been known to occupy part of a kangaroo rat mound while the rodents were still living in the other part—like having an apartment over a favorite restaurant.

The diminutive kit fox displays as much talent for digging as the gray fox lacks. In the relatively loose, sandy soils they prefer, kit fox breeding dens resemble condominiums—they might boast half a dozen entrances and form a sizable mound above the surrounding terrain. The individual holes, though, are small—barely a foot tall and seven inches wide. Kit foxes give birth early, in February and March, and the four or five young are on their own by the end of summer.

Kit fox mother and her litter of pups.

Bringing Home the Bacon

A coyote on a hunting expedition often looks as though it's just goofing off. Like a late-night shopper idly browsing a deli, it trots down a familiar path, relaxed but alert for bargains. If a tiny sound or scent catches its attention, the illusion vanishes as the coyote freezes, every sense focused on the source. A slow creep forward, a sudden rush and pounce—and a mouse, a pack rat, even a grasshopper is snapped up and gobbled down.

Naturalist Hope Ryden once timed a coyote that froze in place when a ground squirrel it was stalking looked up. The coyote remained absolutely rigid—one foot held in the air—for eleven minutes.

Sometimes the result of the hunt is less dramatic: a few dozen juniper berries, some mesquite pods, or a batch of ripe cactus fruit. Even carrion, road-killed or otherwise, is welcomed; in fact, roadsides are a favorite foraging route for coyotes, sometimes with dire consequences. Only occasionally does the coyote's diet include large prey such as deer, and on rare occasions livestock, though they will take fawns or calves that are left unguarded.

On the rare occasions they do take big game, coyotes will hunt in pairs or a pack. They also have been known to take turns running down smaller, but more fleet targets such as jackrabbits. And scientists have only recently confirmed what Native Americans had long observed: coyotes frequently "cooperate" with badgers,

which are champion excavators, to hunt burrowing animals such as ground squirrels. Typically the coyote will hang around while the badger digs. If the prey pops out another hole the coyote grabs it and runs. But apparently the coyote's presence often forces the squirrel to stay underground, giving the badger a better chance at it—so both species could benefit from the arrangement. Researchers have even reported coyotes *herding* badgers toward likely burrows.

Coyotes have long been condemned as stock killers. In southern Arizona they certainly have the opportunity to live up to that reputation, since thousands of square miles of private and public lands are grazed by cattle. But the chances of a coyote—even a group of coyotes—taking down an adult cow are slim. Calves are more vulnerable, but normally their mothers can defend them effectively. Only in parts of the country where sheep are raised is coyote predation a major problem. Rather than using traps and poison, some ranchers are using guard dogs and, reputedly even more effective, guard llamas.

One photograph taken by a government trapper—who later quit his job and began speaking out against predator control programs—confirms at least one coyote's innocence as a threat to most livestock. The photo shows the dead coyote with the contents of its stomach laid out neatly on the ground: 19 mice and one kangaroo rat, the result of a single morning's hunting. This supports what a researcher from Kansas State University calculated one coyote might eat in a year, not counting vegetable material: 160 rabbits, or 3,000 kangaroo rats, or 5,000 mice.

Coyotes dine democratically, from deer to deer mice, and from grasshoppers to grass. This one has snatched a Gambel's quail.

Predators & People

RELATIONSHIPS BETWEEN *predators and humans have long been uneasy. Since livestock was introduced to North America we have worked hard to protect them from predation; efforts continue today, including government-sponsored predator killing. In 1994 in Arizona, federal agents killed 1,528 coyotes, eight gray foxes and a kit fox (as well as mountain lions, bears, badgers and bobcats), spending $700,000. Control pressure has affected wild canines differently: fox populations have been affected little, Mexican wolves are nearly extinct and coyote numbers have increased overall.*

Like the coyote, the gray fox is an opportunistic omnivore. In both species, the contents of their diet can change depending on the time of year: in spring, they exploit exploding rodent populations; when fruits and nuts of plants are ripening, they may adopt a more herbivorous menu. Both will munch happily on reptiles and arthropods, and neither will pass up carrion. The climbing ability of the gray fox allows it to add bird eggs and nestlings to the plate. Naturalist Ernest Thompson Seton once spotted a gray fox, apparently taking a break from foraging, resting in an abandoned hawk's nest a full thirty feet off the ground, while in Arizona they have been found sleeping in the crotch of a saguaro cactus arm.

This gray fox was the victim of a leg-hold trap. These traps are now banned on public lands in Arizona.

Ironically, given its size—the smallest fox in North America—the tiny kit fox is more purely carnivorous than the gray fox or coyote. A large part of its diet consists of kangaroo rats, small rodents with large hind legs that enable them to hop like their namesakes. Since their habitat can include areas of soft sand, kangaroo rats have evolved thick fur between their toes to gain flotation—an adaptation shared by the kit foxes that pursue them. Most species of kangaroo rats are active all year in southern Arizona, supplying the fox with a steady food source. Kit foxes also prey upon ground squirrels, mice, cottontail rabbits, and even jackrabbits—which must be quite a battle, since the prey outweighs the predator. It's been reported that, when digging out ground squirrels, kit foxes will first plug the escape holes in the rodent's burrow system before excavating. They are also adept at catching lizards and even scorpions, deftly crushing the stinging end before crunching the rest.

A problem faced by all desert animals is daytime heat combined with the scarcity of water. By foraging largely at night the coyote, gray and kit foxes take advantage of cooler temperatures (as do the animals they hunt). The three also share the ability to gain much of their moisture requirements from the bodies of their prey. The kit fox takes this adaptation to the extreme: in some parts of its range it rarely drinks, and the kangaroo rats on which it subsists need never drink, relying solely on water they manufacture from carbohydrates in the dry seeds they eat.

The oak and pine-oak woodland that was preferred by the Mexican wolf is also the habitat of its primary

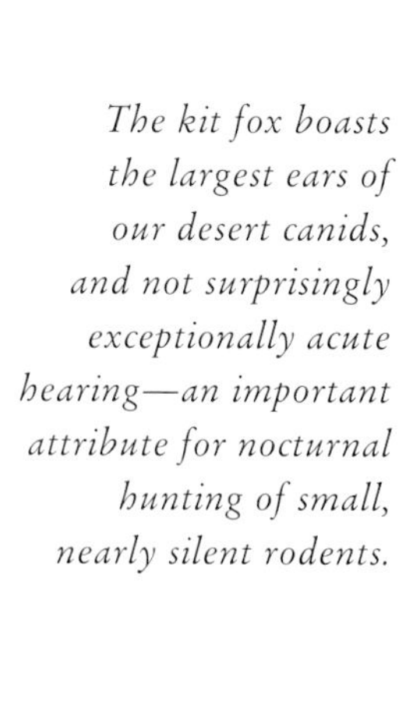

The kit fox boasts the largest ears of our desert canids, and not surprisingly exceptionally acute hearing—an important attribute for nocturnal hunting of small, nearly silent rodents.

A coyote pack hunts for a meal among flocks of sandhill cranes and snow geese.

prey, the Coues' white-tailed deer. This subspecies of the white-tailed deer is small—males average about 80 pounds, females only 65—relatively easy for a single wolf or a pair to bring down. The larger mule deer, which ranges up into the oak woodlands, would be taken as well when the opportunity arose, and probably young elk, pronghorn and bighorn sheep, which at one time were more common in Mexican wolf habitat. Although wolves occasionally killed small game such as rabbits, they habitually chose larger hoofed animals—a preference that spelled trouble when domestic livestock was introduced.

Although wolves, like coyotes, seldom killed full-grown cattle, unprotected calves and yearlings were vulnerable. As the cattle herds expanded, ranchers began complaining of losses—a complaint that brought in the federal government and its campaign of eradication. Sportsmen were firmly on the side of the ranchers; even the great conservationist Aldo Leopold wrote in the early 1900s of the benefits to deer populations—and thus hunters—if wolves could be eliminated. By the time Leopold changed his mind, it was too late for the Mexican wolves on the U.S. side of the border.

The wolves were gone, but the cattle stayed, and now the potential for renewed conflict has been raised for wolves that might be restored to their former range. To minimize wolf-cow interaction, proposed reintroduction areas are in remote areas; to offset economic damage for ranchers, a fund to reimburse them for documented cattle losses has been set up by Defenders of Wildlife, and under a special provision proposed by U.S. Fish and Wildlife, problem wolves could be removed or killed.

Calls of the Wild

Scientists like to find rational explanations for behavior in animals. They take it for granted that all behavior has a purpose, some function that helps the animal to survive, else it would not have evolved in the first place. Nature wastes very little energy.

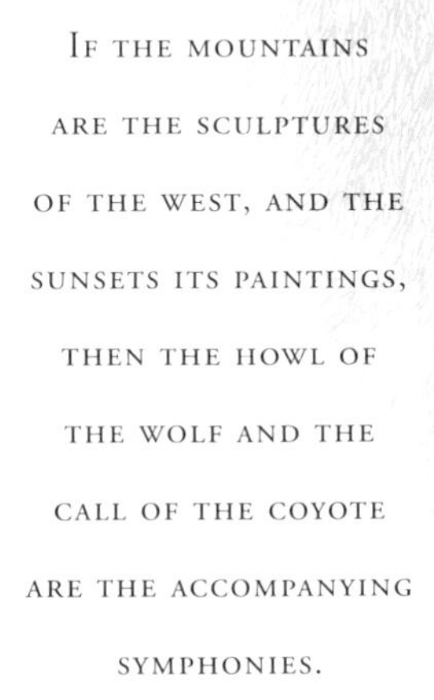

If the mountains are the sculptures of the West, and the sunsets its paintings, then the howl of the wolf and the call of the coyote are the accompanying symphonies.

It is clear that howling serves several important functions for both coyotes and wolves. It helps members of the pack locate each other or call in siblings and offspring. It advertises the territory of the group to other packs. And some researchers think it may reinforce pack bonds before—or after—a group hunt. But there is also very little doubt that these animals sometimes howl just for the infectious joy of howling. Again and again observers have witnessed groups of wolves or coyotes surrender to exuberant explosions of synchronized howling—then go right back to the naps they were taking beforehand. Useful though it may be at times, howling also seems to be the canine answer to singing in the shower, or perhaps karaoke.

For wild canines like this coyote, howling may be for pleasure as well as comminication.

A remarkable component of the howl is the multi-tonal spread of notes; that is, it may rise and fall and catch like a yodel over a range of an octave or more. When two animals howl together the combined effect of this gives the impression of a whole group. It's an illusion especially noticeable with coyotes, who punctuate their howls with much yapping and yipping. Three or four coyotes together sound like at least a dozen.

Vocalization, of which howling is only one facet, has evolved with two other forms of communication—body language and scent marking—to give coyotes, foxes and wolves an intricate range of expression. Scientists stop well short of calling these various means of expressing alarm, dominance, territory, etc. a *language*, but there is no doubt the message gets across clearly.

Kit and gray foxes don't howl, but they share other vocalizations with coyotes and wolves. Whining and growling are used by all canids as short-range messages

Bared teeth and a contest of wills are not necessarily serious—to young wild canines like this coyote pup it's part of growing up and learning the intricacies of the pack's social hierarchy.

or warnings, either to mates and offspring, or to other species. Canid pups learn to communicate with whines and growls early on and snarl ferociously at each other over food and playthings. This helps establish a hierarchy among the siblings—a microcosm of later pack structure for coyotes and wolves. Pups will even growl at their parents over food, like teenagers testing the limits of insubordination.

Though foxes, coyotes and wolves can bark, they do so much less often than their domesticated kin. Wolves will sometimes woof softly at the approach of an intruder, and coyotes sometimes yap at each other or at intruders. Kit foxes and gray foxes yip when alarmed, and gray foxes produce some very strange noises, which sound more like the yowling of a cat than anything a canine should utter.

Submissive behavior

Body language is very important in asserting—and accepting—dominance among siblings or pack members. When a domestic dog cringes under its master's tongue-lashing, or rolls over to expose its throat and stomach, it is instinctively displaying the same submissive behavior that a wild relative does to a parent, stronger sibling or dominant pack member. This ritualized posturing is seen whenever pack members come together: the subordinate individuals approach the alpha members in a comically fawning manner, which the dominant animal seems to accept regally. Wolf researchers have also identified and named a bewildering array of facial expressions in their subjects, from arcane subtleties such as the "agonistic pucker" to the more universal "intimidating stare."

Body language is an important part of canine society. This Mexican wolf is recognizing a fellow pack member's dominance.

THE SOUND of coyotes yipping in the night is one of the bonuses of desert living. But what do we do when they join us in our backyards or alleys? William W. Shaw of the University of Arizona, who researches urbanized coyotes, suggests the following tips for living with coyotes:

- *Keep garbage in coyote-proof containers (lids that latch securely).*
- *Don't feed your pets outside where coyotes, or any wild animals, can get to the food.*
- *Vaccinate your pets against rabies, distemper and other canine diseases.*
- *Keep your cats inside at night.*
- *Enjoy them! Coyotes are beautiful animals and they are important hunters and scavengers in the desert ecosystem.*

Native Americans depicted canines in their rock art, like these in a set of petroglyphs in the Tucson Mountains. They also included them in many stories, sometimes embodying mischief, sometimes good, sometimes evil.

It's tempting to interpret all this dominance and submissiveness, snarling and growling and fawning as the signs of a violent society. But in fact an important function of such behavior is to *avoid* violence and possible injury or death among a cooperative family group or pack. While full-blown battles do occur, they are rare; usually the ritualized sequence of point/counterpoint is enough to defuse the situation. For pack animals, dangerous exceptions can include a struggle for the alpha position or an intrusion by a strange individual into the pack's inner territory, called the core area, which they defend vigorously.

Although humans can relate to vocal interaction and body language, our noses are dulled to the richest of all forms of canine communication—scent.

The city-bred poodle drawn irresistibly to the fire hydrant has little chance of carving out its own territory against the efforts of dozens of other dogs. In the wild, though, scent stations function as a detailed classified section: notices of property deeds, postings of personal messages and singles ads (petite female, attractive, 2 yrs. old, seeks good provider with healthy genes).

Whether the hundred-square-mile range of a wolf family or the half-mile-radius circle frequented by a kit fox, scent marking of territory is an important activity. One study recorded alpha wolves marking an average of every two minutes.